Eurovillain Contest
The Secret of Willie Boggins

Published 2000 by BEANObooks geddes & grosset,
an imprint of Children's Leisure Products Limited,
David Dale House, New Lanark ML11 9DJ, Scotland

ISBN 1 84205 005 2

Printed and bound in Italy

EUROVILLAIN CONTEST

MEANWHILE IN A SEMI-DETACHED, SITS LITTLE ERIC, THE BOY WITH THE SEMI-DETACHED BRAIN
BORING RUBBISH! WISH I HAD SATELLITE TV.

OOER — ITS A BIT PRICEY!
SATELLITE DISH 2002

BUT SOON —
HOW DID HE DO IT?
SATELLITE SKY AYE TV

I CAN'T FIND THE WOK, OR MY KNITTING NEEDLES.
I CAN'T FIND THE FLEX FOR MY ELECTRIC DRILL.

I CONSTRUCTED A DO-IT-YOURSELF SATELLITE DISH.

I CAN'T BEAR TO SEE MY PARENTS GETTING UPSET.
HE'S GOING TO CONFESS. WHAT A CARING SON.

NO — I'LL SHUT THE DOOR SO I CAN'T HEAR THEM.
SLAM!

AND NOW, BEJABBERS, TIS TOIME FOR THE EUROVILLAIN CONTEST TO FIND THE BIGGEST VILLAIN IN EUROPE! WE HAVE A NEUTRAL JUDGE —
UNCTIOUS SMIRKE

IT'S KING ZORG — FROM THE PLANET NERK.
HIYA, FANS!

THE JUDGING PANEL HAS BEEN SPECIALLY SELECTED.

THEY ALL WORK FOR ME AND IF THEY DON'T DO AS I SAY, THEY'RE TERMINATED.

ALL THE VILLAINS HAVE TO CHALLENGE BANANAMAN — BUT IT APPEARS HE HAS CHICKENED OUT!

TYPICAL! THESE SUPER-HEROES CAN'T BE RELIED ON!
WATCH THIS!

HOLD IT — I'M BANANAMAN!
QUICK IS'NT HE?

I'M NOT DUE TO APPEAR TILL THURSDAY THE SIXTEENTH AND IT WAS ONLY WEDNESDAY THE FIFTEENTH YESTERDAY.

GULP!
REALISATION SLOWLY DAWNING

GOTTA GIT ME A NANA SHARPISH.

NYICCH! IT'S A PLASTIC FAKE.
FLOOP!

AT THE LARDER —
THIS TASTES LIKE THE GENUINE ARTICLE!

STAND BY FOR TRANSFORMATION
SWOOF!
FABOOM!
NOW WHICH WAY IS EUROPE?
AHA! I'M ON THE RIGHT TRAIL!
THE METHVENS
REST OF EUROPE
WALTERS HOOSE
HM! THICK CLOUD! THAT WON'T STOP ME!
DOVER TO CALAIS DINGY
OH NO?
THUD!
TISK! THIS CLOUD IS THICKER THAN MY GRANNY'S PEA SOUP!
9
AND NANAMAN IS THICKER THAN EITHER

THIS IS THE WORK OF WEATHERMAN, THE METEOROLOGICAL VILLAIN
THE WEATHERSHIP
MY VISION HAS CLOUDED OVER!
BUT —
THEY CAN'T STOP A SUPERHERO.
THE DOCKS
PLEASE TAKE ME OVER ON YOUR NICE FERRY.
IF YOU CAN'T PAY THE FERRYMAN — GET LOST!
SLAM!

IF ONLY THE CHANNEL TUNNEL WAS HERE.
BEWARE OF FROGS!
VERA LYNNE SANG HERE!

TAKE ANOTHER LOOK, BLUE-BLOOMERS
THE OTHER CHANNEL TUNNEL AN' IT'S FREE!

BUT IT'S THE MOLE! PRACTISING FOR THE EUROVILLAIN CONTEST
IT'S
EE!

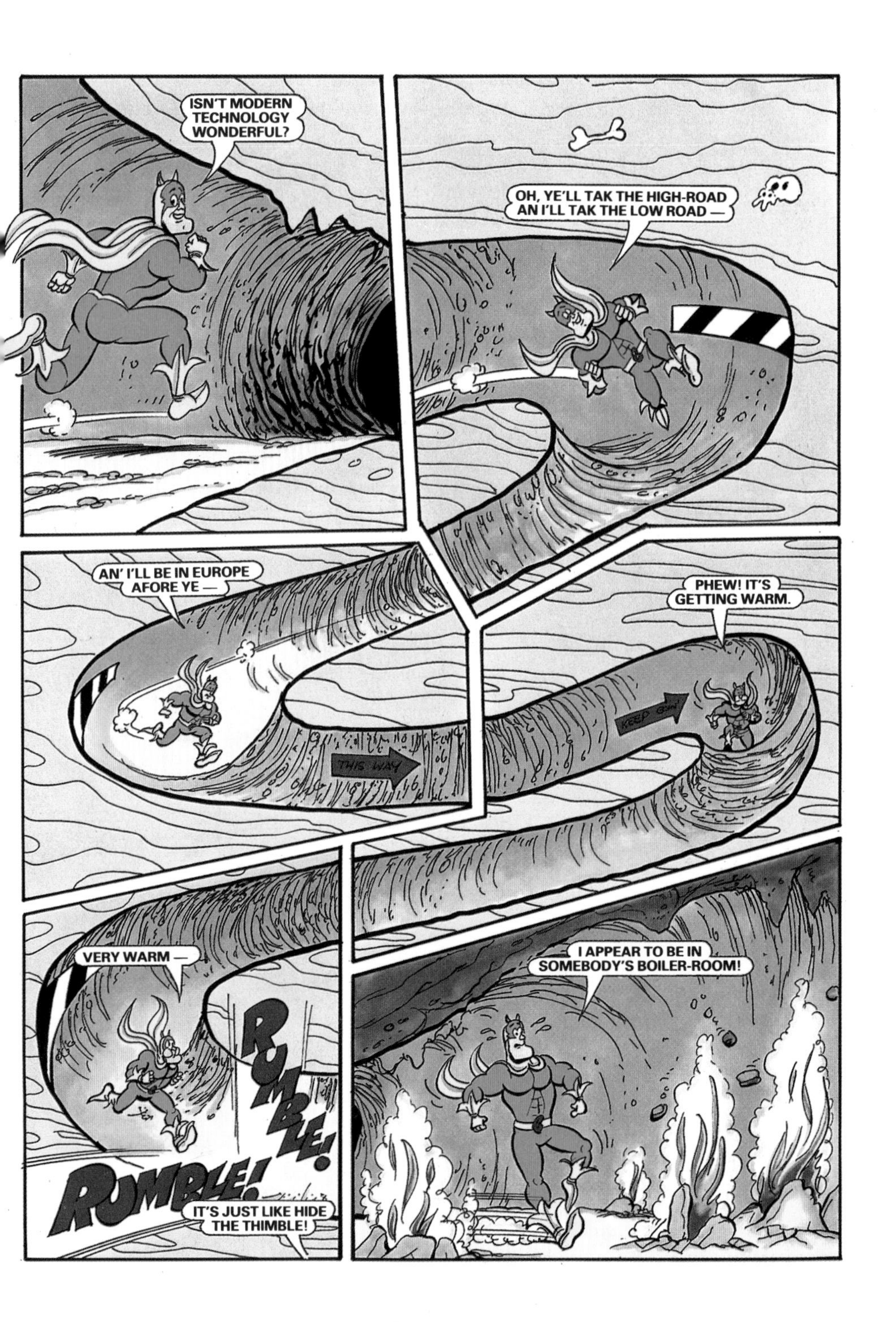
ISN'T MODERN TECHNOLOGY WONDERFUL?
OH, YE'LL TAK THE HIGH-ROAD AN I'LL TAK THE LOW ROAD —
AN' I'LL BE IN EUROPE AFORE YE —
THIS WAY
KEEP GOIN'
PHEW! IT'S GETTING WARM.
VERY WARM —
RUMBLE!
RUMBLE!
IT'S JUST LIKE HIDE THE THIMBLE!
I APPEAR TO BE IN SOMEBODY'S BOILER-ROOM!

KRACK!
VOOOM!
ACTUALLY, HE'S IN THE CENTRE OF THE EARTH

BUT NOT FOR LONG
AAAAGGHH!
FWOOOOSH!
WHOOMP!

BY A STRANGE QUIRK OF FATE, OUR HERO HAS LANDED RIGHT IN THE MIDDLE OF EUROPE
OLE'
THE GOOD NEWS IS — I'M HERE —
SAVE THE SNAIL

THE BAD NEWS IS, I'LL NEVER DO THE LAMBADA AGAIN.
NIRDLE TV

AT THE TV STUDIO
OK, FISH-FACE! LET'S SHOW A BIT OF RESPECT FOR A TRULY GREAT PERSONALITY.

HE'S LEAPING TO HIS FEET.

SALUTING HUMBLY.

THERE'S NO NEED TO OVERDO THE GROVELLING, ZORG!

IT'S NOT YOU — IT'S FOR UNCTIOUS SMIRKE, THE TV PERSONALITY.

YOU'VE HELD THINGS UP FOR LONG ENOUGH! LET THE CONTEST BEGIN.

THE VILLAINS OF EUROPE SHALL NOT OUTWIT THE FORCES OF LAW AND THINGMYBOB.

NOTHING AROUND BUT THIS GIANT SWISS CHEESE!

NOTHING SUSPICIOUS HERE.

YOU SPOKE TOO SOON, MAN IN BLUE!
GASP! IT'S GOUDAMAN! THE BIG CHEESE IN THE EUROVILLAIN SCENE!

YODELEETEEE! CAN'T CATCH ME!
THIS IS NOTHING TO AN OLD POT-HOLER LIKE ME!

MANY TWISTS AND TURNS LATER —
CHEESEY GRIN
PAH! BACK WHERE I STARTED!
WHAT A PLONKER!

I CAN WAIT, GOUDAMAN!
SOME MUSIC WHILE YOU'RE WAITING, NANAMAN?

LITTLE BOY BLUE, COME BLOW UP YOUR HORN!

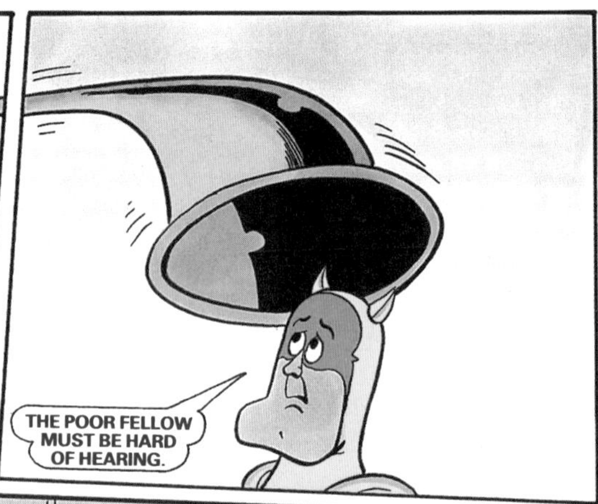
THE POOR FELLOW MUST BE HARD OF HEARING.

PARP!

THIS IS INDEED A NOTEWORTHY VILLAIN.
CRASH!
CRASH!

THESE SOUR-NOTES SMELL OF GORGONZOLA!

NOW FOR ME CHAMPIONSHIP-WINNING PERFORMANCE!

PAAARP!
THAT SOUNDED LIKE A FLAT NOTE.

IT'S BANANAMAN WHO GETS FLATTENED —
WHUMP!

BUT BANANAMAN RISES TO THE OCCASION —
YODELEE! TIME TO FLEE!

I'M NOT FOLLOWING HIM INTO THAT CHEESEY CAVERN.

I'LL HELP MYSELF TO A MORSEL OF CHEESE!

GOUDAMAN IS RELAXING —
AHA! HERE COMES THE WORLD'S MOST USELESS SUPERHERO!
DANISH BLUE MUSK
CHEDDAR CONCERTO

COME IN, BANANAMAN! YOUR TIME IS UP! ARE YOU A MAN OR A MOUSE?

I AM A MAN!
THESE ARE MICE!
MUM-MUM-MUMMICE!
THIS IS AN EXPRESSION OF ABJECT TERROR
CHOMP!
CHOMP!
MUNCH!
CHOMP!
YOU LOOK CHEESED-OFF, MY GOOD FELLOW!
BACK IN THE STUDIO —
WHAT'S THE SCORE FOR GOUDAMAN?

GOUDAMAN, ZERO POINTZ!
GOUDAMAN, NO POINTS —
0 0 0 0 0 0 0 0

AND NOW I GIVE YOU OUR NEXT CONTESTANT! TAKE HIM, PLEASE TAKE HIM.

TIS MOI! GARLICMAN! WATCH ME ROB ZEES BANK.
REAR OF BANK
GARLIC

REAR OF BANK

NOW I AM READEE FOR ACTION!

I DON'T NEED ZE WELDING TORCH!

NOW TO SCOOT WEETH ZE LOOT!

HOLD IT, FROG-BREATH, I MUST ASK YOU TO ACCOMPANY ME!
SACRE BLEU!

HOW WOULD YOU LIKE TO BE DOWN BY THE SEINE WEETH ME?
WIFE AND TRUSS TO SUPPORT

NOT THAT SORT OF ACCOMPANY! YOU'RE NICKED, FROG-FACE!

COP A LOADA THIS, EENGLEESHMAN —

HOH-HOH-HOH-HOH! THAT WAS A NASTY BLOW FOR HEEM!
GASP!
THUD!

BUT SUDDENLY —
HOLD IT! I WANT TO BREATHALYSE YOU!
OOPS! A MAN IN BLEU!

AS I THOUGHT! YOU ARE WELL OVER THE GARLIC LIMIT.

ORDER! ORDER!
BANANAMAN PRONOUNCES JUDGEMENT ON THE FELON.

TWO GARLIC-SAUSAGE ON GARLIC-BREAD, SPREAD WEETH GARLIC-BUTTER, M'LUD.

I'M GONNA THROW THE BOOK AT YOU, GARLICMAN.
WHUMP!
THE BOOK

HO-HO! FOOLED HIM! IT'S NOT A BREATHALYSER — ONLY A PINK BALLOON.
HELD BY A BLUE BUFFOON

GASSP!
THRIPPPPH!

HOW DO OUR PANEL RATE GARLICMAN?

ZILCH!

HM! A LOW-SCORING CONTEST, SO FAR!

NEXT TO GO IS SPAGHETTIMAN FROM ITALIA
I ROBBA DA BANKA!

I CLIMBA DA WALLS
WIT DA SPAGHETTI ROPE!

HUM! THAT SMELLS
LIKE SPAGHETTI
BOLOGNESE!

JUST SOME SPAGHETTEE!
GEEVE EET TO MEE!

DON'T EAT THAT
OR I'LL —

WHEE!
FALLLL!
SPOFF!

I'M GONNA ROBBA
DA SECURICARRA!

WITH A WEB
OF SPAGHETTI!

NOW I HAVE THEM
AT MY MERCY!

NOT SO FAST, SPAGHETTIMAN.
CURSES!

YUM-YUM! BANANA-FLAVOURED. THAT'S MY FAVOURITE!
MUTTER

WHAT VILLAINY ARE YOU PLANNING NOW?
I'VE GIVEN UP VILLAINY.

YOU'VE MADE MY SPAGHETTI SO POPULAR I'VE OPENED A CARRY-OUT.
BAH! YOU CAN'T TRUST ANYONE THESE DAYS.

OK — BACK TO THE STUDIO!
THE DEADLY SHRIMP
PART IV.

NEXT, IS IVAN THE TERRIBLE! THE RUSSIAN ROBBER!

IN THE BANK —
I'M READY FOR ANYTHING!

THIS IS A HOLD-UPSKI!
TSK! NAUGHTY!

BAH! MY BRACES HAVE BURSTSKI!
HO-HO! IT REALLY IS A HOLD-UP NOW.

NOBODY AROUND? GOODSKI!

NOW FOR SOME SMASH AND GRABITOV -
BRICK

EH!
WHAT'S GOING ON?

NNYMMMPH!

IS THERE A DENTIST IN THE HOUSE?

WAH! I'M TERRIBLE! JUST TERRIBLE!
POOR FELLOW! HE'S WEEPING BUCKETS!

I'LL SHOW YOU HOW TO BE A SUCCESSFUL VILLAIN. WATCH ME PINCH THIS LITTLE GIRL'S ICE-CREAM.
NO CHANCE!

SCUFFLE!
HO-HO! I'M NOT SO TERRIBLE AFTER ALL!

I THINK THE PANEL ARE ABOUT TO GIVE THEIR OPINION ON IVAN THE TERRIBLE!

RASP!
QUITE SO!

NEXT IT'S ABZORBA THE GREEK —
KEBABS

I BECOME HARD AS A BRICK WHEN I TOUCH A BRICK WALL.

I BELIEVE THICK AS A BRICK IS THE EXPRESSION.

I SOON DEMOLISHED THAT VILLAIN!
CRUMP!

BUT HE ABSORBS THE METAL BALL –
NOW I'M A MAN OF STEEL!
OOPS! I'VE DROPPED A CLANGER!

I'LL ROCK THAT TIN-MAN TO HIS FOUNDATIONS

BUT ABZORBA ABSORBS ALL THE ROCKS!
CORKS! HE'S GOT A FACE OF STONE AND A GRANITE JAW.

EXTRA! EXTRA! FAMOUS ARTIST GUILTY OF BLACK PUDDIN' SMUGGLING!
GET YER PAPERS 'ERE
AHA! PAPER!

ABSORB THAT LOT, BRICK-BONCE!

NOW TO MAKE HIM ALL SOGGY!

NOW YOU'VE BECOME PAPER-MACHE-MAN!
SPALOOSH!
I'VE WATERED-DOWN THAT CHALLENGE!
GLOOP! I'M DISSOLVING!
AND YET ANOTHER CHALLENGER SINKS WITHOUT TRACE.
NEXT IN IS CHINAMAN —
YING-TONG TIDDLE!
EH?
SORRY, PAL! CHINA'S NOT IN EUROPE!
SINCE WHEN?
NOT IN EUROPE — I'M SHATTERED.
!
DON'T WORRY, MY LITTLE ORIENTAL CHUM!
SLAP!
SHATTER!
NOW HE REALLY IS SHATTERED!
FINEST BONE CHINA

AND NOW INTRODUCING A SPECIAL GUEST STAR, YOUR ENEMY AND MINE, THE ARCH-VILLAIN DOCTOR GLOOM!
HE'S GOT HIS VAPORISER —
I'LL VAPORISE THE SUPPORTS.
NOW TO SETTLE BANANAMAN'S HASH!
YOO-HOO! BLUE-BLOOMERS! WHERE ARE YOU?
BANANAMAN JUST HAPPENS TO BE JOGGING PAST —
OOPS! HOW CLUMSY OF ME!
CLUNK!
YOU'VE DROPPED YOUR TORCH — HOPE IT ISN'T BROKEN!
CLICK! CLICK!
I MUST FLEE BEFORE HE VAPORISES ANYTHING ELSE!
HOW STRANGE!

WE CAN SEE THE PANEL'S OPINION ON DOCTOR GLOOM.
GONE TO LUNCH

AND NEXT WE HAVE —

A DRAGON! WHO DRAGGED THAT IN HERE?

IT'S A VIKING LONG-SHIP!

'TIS I, THE NORSEMAN.

YOU'LL DO NO PILLAGING WHEN I'M AROUND.
WHO CHALLENGES RAGNAR THE HAIRY?

PREPARE TO BECOME A BANANA-SPLIT!

SLASH!
NOT SO FAST, HAIRY-FACE!

FANCY A SLICE OF DANISH BLUE?
NOT TODAY.

ALLOW ME TO TRIM YOUR TOENAILS!
NO THANKS.

MISSED!

OH, YEAH! WHAT'S THIS 'EAR?

VICTORY TO NORSEMAN!

I'LL JUST ADJUST THIS SATELLITE DISH.

NYARRGH! WHAT'S HAPPENING?
BLEEP!
BLEEP!

SOMEBODY SWITCH ME OFF!
NOT UNTIL 'NEIGHBOURS' IS FINISHED!

HOW DO YOU RATE THE NORSEMAN?

THERE'S NOTHING GOOD ON THE TELLY THESE DAYS.
0 0 0 0 0 0 0 0

AND NOW A BREAK FROM THE EUROVILLAIN CONTEST FOR THE WEATHER FORECAST.

THERE WILL BE RAIN, FOG, SNOW, HAIL, MIST, FOG AND HURRICANES —

IT'S WEATHERMAN AT HIS WORST —
EVERYBODY TALKS ABOUT THE WEATHER. SO I'LL GIVE THEM PLENTY TO TALK ABOUT!
NIRDLE TV
EVENIN' ALL! BIT PARKY!

I'LL TRY TO REASON WITH HIM.
THIS IS THE WORST SPELL OF WEATHER IN EUROPE.
NO IT'S NOT!
WHAT DID THE BLUE-BUFFOON MEAN BY THAT?
HERE'S SMIFFY FROM BASH STREET.
TWO BRAINLESS FOOLS TOGETHER.
SPELL 'WEATHER', SMIFFY.
I DON'T KNOW WEATHER I CAN.
W-E-V-V-I-R!
THERE — THAT'S THE WORST SPELL OF WEATHER IN EUROPE!
I'M OFF TO MELT THE ARCTIC CIRCLE.
CLEVER BOY, SMIFFY.
A SELDOM-HEARD UTTERANCE.
ANY POINTS FOR WEATHERMAN?
WEATHERMAN FAILS TO GET THE POINT!

MEANWHILE, IN A GARAGE, BIG RITA WATCHES WHILE SHE WORKS —
THAT ROTTEN PANEL HAVEN'T GIVEN ANY POINTS.

THEY MAKE ME SO MAD!
CLUNG
THUNG!

REALLY MAD!

HAS MY CAR PASSED ITS MOT TEST?

HERE'S YOUR CAR!
FLICK!

I'M OFF TO THE TV STUDIOS TO COMPLAIN.
I PRESUME IT FAILED.

IT LOOKS LIKE A DEAD-HEAT FOR EUROVILLAIN OF THE YEAR.

WHERE ARE THOSE NERKS?
CALM YOURSELF, MADAM!

THAT'S FOR GIVING THEM NO MARKS.

WELL, RITA'S CERTAINLY GIVEN THE PANEL PLENTY OF MARKS!

I'M RITA THE PANEL-BEATER AND I'VE JUST BEATEN THE PANEL!

SHE'S A VIOLENT VILLAIN — DO SOMETHING, BANANAMAN.

RITA, A WORD IN YOUR TINY SHELL-PINK EAR.
HE FANCIES ME!

FANCY A DATE, BOY-BLUE?
ER — HARRUMPH! I'LL PASS!

RITA, THE PANEL-BEATER! I DECLARE YOU EUROVILLAIN OF THE YEAR!
I RESIGN AS CHAIRMAN!
WOT A SWIZZ!

Comic Capers

THE GREAT CITY SLEEPS! IT HIDES A GREAT SECRET DOWN IN NOT-SO-GREAT ACACIA ROAD . . .
The SECRET of Willie Boggins
A BANANAMAN adventure! (Honest!)

. . . FOR BEHIND THE DOOR AT NUMBER TWENTY-FOUR . . .
24

. . . LIVES A GREAT LITTLE LAD! GREAT STUFF THIS, HUH!
24

AND HERE HE IS! THE EXTRA-GREAT WILLIE BOGGINS!
BURRP!
PICKLED EGGS

HOI! WAIT A BIT! THIS BOOK IS ALL ABOUT ME, ERIC WIMP, ALIAS BANANAMAN, RIGHTER OF WRONGS, HANDSOME, FEARLESS . . .

GERROFF! WE'RE SICK OF SEEIN' YOU!!
VOOM!
BAM!

SLUGE!

NOT A GOOD START, IS IT, FANS?

SCHLOP!
NEEAAGH! WHAT ELSE CAN GO WRONG?

SLAM!

!
ASK A SILLY QUESTION . . !! OOOOOH!

IS ERIC WIMP GONE FOR GOOD? GOOD!
!!!

CONTINUE WITH THE FILM! TAKE TWOOOO . . .
THWACK!
OOOOH!

BUT WILLIE BOGGINS HIDES A DARK, DARK SECRET!
'E DOES INDEED, MOOSH!
THROB!

. . . FOR WHEN WILLIE EATS A PICKLED EGG . . .
GLURK!

WILLIE IS TRANSFORMED . . . WILLIE IS . . .
FIZZZ!
KRAAKK!
. . . WILLIE IS . . .

. . . GENERAL BLIGHT!!??

THE VERY ONE! GENERAL BLIGHT IT IS! WHO WAS YOU EXPECTIN'?
MY EGGY BREATH'S BEEN TOO MUCH FOR THE POOR FOOL!
THUD!
SSST! SSST!
EGGY DEODERANT
THIS IS OUR LITTLE SECRET, READERS! BANANAMAN'S NOT THE ONLY ONE WITH A SECRET IDENTITY!
BUT FOR NOW, IF YOU'LL JUST EXCUSE ME I'LL FINISH OFF MY TRIPE 'N' BLACK PUDDIN' BREAKFAST!
OO, HE'S WICKED, HE IS!
SECOND HELPING

OI! WOTCHOO DOIN' IN 'ERE? WHERE'S MY WILLIE . . . AN' WOT YOU DOIN' EATIN' HIS BREAKFAST?
MA BOGGINS

WHAT ARE YOU GOING TO DO ABOUT IT?

GERROFF WI' YOU, SILLY MAN!
PHONG!

GENERAL BLIGHT! WHAT'S HE DOING IN ACACIA ROAD?

OO'S THIS NOW, MUCKIN' UP ME TIDY YARD?
HI, MISSUS BOGGINS!

CAN I OFFER TO TIDY UP?

I'LL TIDY UP M'SELF, STARTIN' WI' YOU . . . AN' IF YOU SEE OUR WILLIE, TELL 'IM 'IS BREAKFAST'S GETTIN' COLD!
PHWANG!
AN ACE! GOOD SHOT, MADAM!
AAAGH! MY BOT BONE!!
10
7

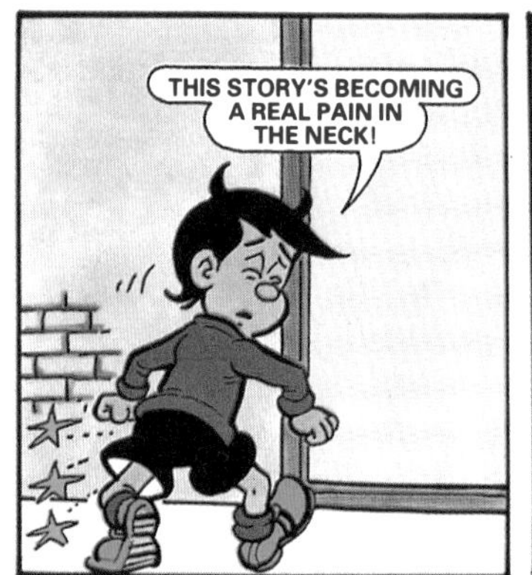
THIS STORY'S BECOMING A REAL PAIN IN THE NECK!

I'LL GET A BANANA AND INVESTIGATE!

BUT, FIRST . . .

. . . I'LL USE THE PEEL AS A PLASTER!

NOW FOR THE BIT YOU'VE ALL BEEN WAITING FOR!

BANANAMAN!
RIP!
TEAR!

BLIGHT'S IN TROUBLE NOW! NOTHING CAN STOP ME!
FLIPPIN' NORAH! CAN'T YOU TAKE YOUR CLOTHES OFF BEFORE YOUR AMAZIN' TRANSFORMATION! THIS IS THE TENTH SET OF CLOTHES YOU'VE RIPPED THIS WEEK, ERIC!
BOP!
MRS WIMP, AN IRATE MOTHER!
OOH! THAT'S SOME LUMP! I'M OFF BALANCE!
YIKES!
SKID!
THUD!
THAT'S BETTER! I'M LEVEL AGAIN!
NOW TO FIND THE GENERAL!

G'BYE, MUM!
OOH! IT'S BANANAMAN!
AIN'T HE DISHY!
I WONDER WHAT HIS SECRET IDENTITY IS?

NOW, WHERE CAN BLIGHT BE? HE'LL BE LYING LOW, I'LL BET! BUT I'LL FLY LOW AND FIND HIM!
I CAN FLY REALLY LOW, Y'KNOW!
YOU'LL HAVE TO!
I CAN FLY UNDER BUSES!
LOWER STILL!
UNDER MINIS AS YOU SEE!
I CAN EVEN FLY UNDER CARS WITH FANCY SKIRTS!
THIS ONE'S REALLY LOW, BUT I'VE DONE IT . . .

. . . ALTHOUGH I MUST ADMIT I'VE SINGED MY AMAZING Y-FRONTS!
OH, NO!
EVEN I CAN'T FLY UNDER THAT!

SPLAT!

OOOOOOH! THAT HURT!

WHERE IS THAT IDIOT NANAMAN?

I'M A BIT FLAT AT THE MOMENT . . .

. . . BUT I DON'T TAKE LONG TO GET BACK INTO SHAPE!
WOP!

WHAT'S UP NOW? BROKEN BONES?
READER'S VOICE

NO! BLIGHT'S BIKE'S MARKED MY NEWEST COZZIE!

OH, GET ON WITH IT! YOU'RE A SUPERSTAR!
YOU'RE RIGHT! I AM! TALLY-HO!

WHERE ARE YOU OFF TO, HERO? IS BLIGHT UP IN THE SKY?

WHUMP!
CLOUD BURST
I'M GETTING MY COSTUME WASHED!

I HAVE TO GET RID OF THOSE NASTY TYRE MARKS!
SPOFF!

NOW FOR A QUICK TRIP TO THE GOOD OL' U.S. OF A . . .
TEXAS

. . . TO SPIN-DRY MY OUTFIT! WHEEEE . . .

BACK TO BLIGHTY AND BLIGHT NOW . . . FLYING OVER THE Q.E.2 . . .
. . . I LOVE THE HEAT OFF THE FUNNELS! TICKLES MY TUMMY!
AW, CUT OUT THE COMEDY AND GET ON WITH CATCHING BLIGHT!
DON'T TAKE THE CRITICISM SO HARD!
'S NOT THAT . . .
. . . I'M CHANGING BACK TO LITTLE ERIC . . .
FOOM
ZUP!
. . . AND LITTLE ERIC'S GOT NO CLOTHES ON!
HELP!!
COMING DOWN . . .

ZOOP!

WHAT'S THIS?
ER . . . HELLO! NICE DAY! I'M ERIC! GOOD JOB YOU'VE GOT BIG SHORTS!

SHOULDN'T YOU BE LOOKING WHERE YOU'RE GOING!

AAAAAIIEE . . .
FONG!

YIKES! I'M AWAY AGAIN!
TWANG!

I DON'T THINK I LIKE THIS . . .

STILL, I'M HOME! I'LL HEAD IN TOWARDS THE SHORE AT SPEED!

OOPS! SORRY, FOLKS! 'SCUSE ME!

AAAAGH!
CHA
CHO

A BANANA! GULP!

NOW FOR A DRAMATIC TRANSFORMATION . . . AND NOT A MOMENT TOO SOON!

FAZOOM!

NOW TO GET BADDIE BLIGHT!
BOO! HISS! PEST!

MEANWHILE—
NO SIGN OF THAT BLUE-UNDIED BALLOON, BANANAMAN . . .

. . . SO I'LL JUST GO RELIEVE THE BANK OF THEIR CASH!
BANK OF BERKS

HAND OVER ALL YOUR MONEY! THIS IS AN UP-HOLD!
WATER PISTOL

HAW! HAW! THAT'S ONLY A WATER PISTOL, GENERAL!
AN OBSERVANT CHAPPIE! BUT A FOOL!

IT'S FILLED WITH DANDY OFFICE COFFEE!
SPOFF!

THERE'S NO KNOWN CURE! EE, I AM AN EVIL OLD BLIGHT!
ERKLE!

TWENTY MORE, TWENTY MORE . . .
I'M TIRED OF PLANS TO TAKE OVER THE WORLD . . . I JUST WANT THE CASH!!
SEE YA, SUCKERS!
OH, NO! I'M CHANGIN' BACK TO LITTLE WILLIE!

WOOF!
WHAT ROTTEN LUCK!
WHERE'S THE ROBBER?

OH, THE VILLAIN WITH THE TIN HAT? HE . . . HE W . . . WENT THATAWAY!
FOLLOW ME, STAFF!

PHEW! IT'S HEAVY CARRYING ALL THIS MONEY AS WILLIE BOGGINS!

WHAT HAVE YOU GOT IN THAT SACK, MY BOY?
IT'S MY TUCK SHOP MONEY, OFFICER!

LET ME HELP YOU TO THE TUCK SHOP! YOU MUST HAVE A BIG, SWEET TOOTH!
NOT REALLY . . .

DAVES
CHIPINN
PICKLED EGGS ARE MY FAVOURITE!

MEANWHILE, THE BLUE GOON IS IN ACACIA ROAD . . .
GENERAL BLIGHT COULD BE ANYWHERE! I'LL TRY IN HERE!
KNOCK! KNOCK!

HAVE YOU SEEN THIS MAN, MADAM?
COUSIN WILLIE

SORRY! NEVER CLAPPED EYES ON HIM, MISS!
THANKS FOR YOUR HELP!

KIN'LY IGNORE THIS NOTICE BY ORDER. A. TWIT TOWN CLOWK
THIS IS SERIOUS! HE'S JUST DISAPPEARED!

HERE HE IS, FOLKS, IN THE ACACIA ROAD CHIPPY!
MENU CHIPS & DEEP SEA TRAFFIC CONES IN
AIN'T YOU GOT ANYTHING SMALLER THAN A £100 NOTE?
PICKLED EGGS

OH, JUST GIVE ME THE WHOLE JAR — KEEP THE CHANGE!

SLUG!
JELLIED SLOTH.
BEANS ON FROG SOP.

KERLUMP!

KRUMP!
I'M A GIANT THANKS TO ALL THOSE EGGIES!
SHATTER!
AH! MY EXTRA-SHARP VISION HAS SPOTTED BLIGHT AT LAST!
KIPPERS & CUSTARD
SUEDE SANDWICHES TO ORDER
EEEK!
OUR FOOD CARRIES A GOVERNMENT HEALTH WARNING
VOOM!

I'VE GOT YOU NOW, YOU BAD EGG!

BEIN' THIS SIZE, I'M SCARED OF NO ONE, ESPECIALLY LITTLE YOU, BLUE DRAWERS!
HE'S GOT A GOOD POINT THERE!

THE BIGGER THEY COME, THE HARDER THEY FALL . . .
KICK!

. . . USUALLY! WAAA! MY TOES!
THROB!

I'LL PUT ON THESE BIG WORK BOOTS! THAT'LL HELP!

PREPARE TO TOPPLE, GENERAL!
CLUMPITTY! CLUMPITTY!

HAW! HAW! EVEN STEEL BOOTS WON'T HURT ME, NANABOY!

OH, I DON'T INTEND TO KICK YOU THIS TIME!
SPARK!
SLIDE!

HOT STUFF, HUH?
I'M ON FIRE!

GOOD JOB A BIG GENERAL HAS A BIG TIN HELMET!

THERE! THE HEAT'S OFF!
SPOFF!
SSSSCH!

I THOUGHT I'D COOKED HIS GOOSE!
YOU'RE A DAMP SQUIB, SHORTY!

SHAKE! SHAKE!
ENOUGH OF THESE GAMES! DOWN YOU GO LIKE THE BEANSTALK GIANT!
CLANG!
HARD LUCK! MY HELMET WINS AGAIN!
NOW TO CRUSH YOU LIKE THE LITTLE BEETLE YOU ARE! SAY G'BYE!

MISSED! CURSES!
TWO CAN PLAY THIS BIG GAME!
RESH RUIT
THUD!

I'LL TAKE ALL YOUR BANANAS, SIR! HERE'S AN OLD POUND — KEEP THE CHANGE!
FRESH BANANAS
SNOFF 2p A TON

FIRST, OFF WITH ALL THE 'NANA PEEL . . .
TRY OUR DELICIOUS PLUM STONES 50p TON DELIVERED.

. . . OUT THEY GO!

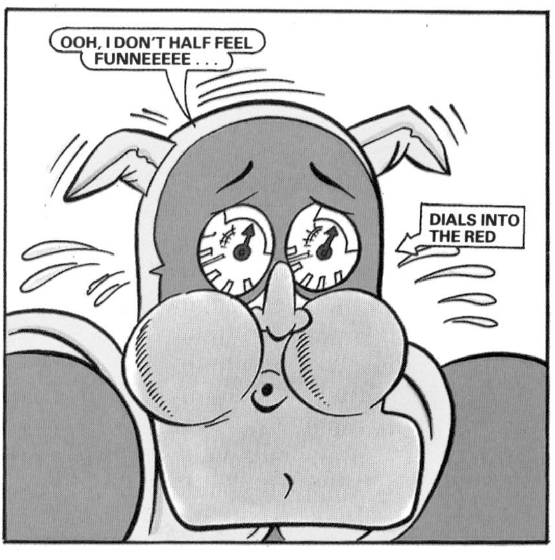
OOH, I DON'T HALF FEEL FUNNEEEEE . . .
DIALS INTO THE RED

NOW FOR THE BIG FIGHT!
WHUMP!
R-R-RIP!
I AM DEAD TALL ✓ O.K.
FRESH FRUIT Co
DO NOT WRITE 'ERE
WOT SHALL I WRITE THEN
OUR FRUIT IS HAND SHOT
A THE PEACHES!
HE'S GETTIN' WORSE! ALL HE USED TO BUST WAS HIS SHORTS!

IT'S SHOWDOWN TIME, TINY!

FOLLOW THE YELLOW BRICK ROAD! WHEEEEE . . .
SKID!

HOWZAT FOR THE GRAND SLAM!!
ZUMP!

SEE, BIG 'NANA BEATS BAD EGG!

NOW, YOU GOTTA GO TO THE BIG COP SHOP!
NOT THE COP SHOP, BUT I SURE GOTTA GO . . .

I JUST GOTTA GO!
GO WHERE?
RUMBLE!

TO THE LITTLE BOYS' ROOM, YOU IDIOT! ALL THOSE EGGIES HAVE UPSET MY TUMMY!
HERE'S A NICE BLUE TOILET!
I'M A GIANT! I NEED SOMETHING BIGGER — AN' FAST!

I'LL HELP YOU, IF YOU PROMISE TO GIVE YOURSELF UP AFTERWARDS!
ANYTHIN'... ONLY HURRY!

THERE'S A POWER STATION COOLING TOWER OVER THERE AND... HOI! READERS! NO LOOKIN' NOW!

I'M SURE YOU'D MUCH RATHER END ON A DRAMATIC PICTURE OF ME...

...ONLY I GOTTA GO, TOO! ALL THOSE 'NANA'S! HURRY UP, GENERAL!
WHOOSH!
THE END
(HONEST!)

Comic Capers

Zob

Zob

Last Laugh

Comic Capers
BEANO books
geddes & grosset